OXFORD
UNIVERSITY PRESS

Great Clarendon Street, Oxford OX2 6DP

Oxford University Press is a department of the University of
Oxford. It furthers the University's objective of excellence in
research, scholarship, and education by publishing worldwide in

Oxford   New York

Athens   Auckland   Bangkok   Bogotá   Buenos Aires
Calcutta   Cape Town   Chennai   Dar es Salaam   Delhi
Florence   Hong Kong   Istanbul   Karachi   Kuala Lumpur
Madrid   Melbourne   Mexico City   Mumbai   Nairobi   Paris
São Paulo   Singapore   Taipei   Tokyo   Toronto   Warsaw

with associated companies in   Berlin   Ibadan

Oxford is a registered trade mark of Oxford University Press
in the UK and in certain other countries

British Library Cataloguing in Publication Data

ISBN 0–19–276219 2

Printed in Great Britain by Biddles Limited
Guildford and King's Lynn

A-Haunting We Will Go

& other spooky rhymes

Written by
Nicholas Tulloch

Illustrated by
Chris Mould

Contents

A Haunting We Will Go!

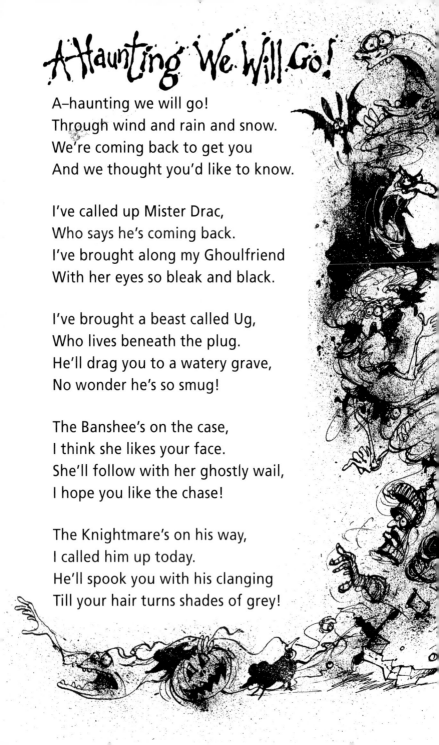

A-haunting we will go!
Through wind and rain and snow.
We're coming back to get you
And we thought you'd like to know.

I've called up Mister Drac,
Who says he's coming back.
I've brought along my Ghoulfriend
With her eyes so bleak and black.

I've brought a beast called Ug,
Who lives beneath the plug.
He'll drag you to a watery grave,
No wonder he's so smug!

The Banshee's on the case,
I think she likes your face.
She'll follow with her ghostly wail,
I hope you like the chase!

The Knightmare's on his way,
I called him up today.
He'll spook you with his clanging
Till your hair turns shades of grey!

And Frankenstein is here,
So let me make it clear;
Despite his silly square-shaped head,
He'll have you filled with fear!

And finally let me say,
We'll scare you every day.
And now we've made a comeback,
We've decided we should stay!

A–haunting we will go!
Through wind and rain and snow.
We're coming back to get you
And we thought you'd like to know...

Spooky Bat

Spooky bat, spooky bat
What d'you think you're playing at?
All those hours in your cave
You've practised how to misbehave.
Enid Jones, who lives downstairs,
Says you caught her unawares.
Nothing's clever, nothing's big
In building nests inside her wig.
Harold Smith, from down the lane
Tells me you're an awful pain.
Harold's nice, but still you chose
To lick his ears and bite his nose!
And what about Tobias Shaw,
The friendly chap who lives next door?
He'd like to have a word or two
About that *brown stuff* in his shoe.
Perhaps by hanging upside-down
You've scrambled all your brains around.
Your slant on life is oddly-viewed,
Where laughs are had by being rude.
And pleasure? I can see that that's
By driving all your neighbours bats.

A Mummy's Curse

It made the Mummy
Really cross
That from his stone
Sarcophagus,
Some greedy thieves
Had robbed his gold,
And dared disturb
His Sacred Hold.
And then the Mummy
Swore aloud,
Which sounded muffled
Through his shroud.
It made me wonder
Which is worse:
An angry Mummy,
Or his curse?

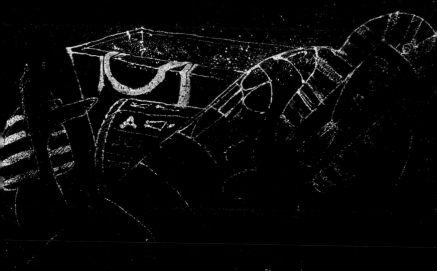

Feeling Fine

Whenever the night
Is still and cold
And darkness fills the air,
When witches zoom
Towards the moon
I find I do not care.

And when with shrieks
And howls and cries
Mere mortals are engrossed,
I'm feeling fine
And glad that I'm
Still proud to be
A ghost.

Silas

I knew a ghost called Silas,
Who lived inside my wireless.
I couldn't seem to switch him off,
He'd always been quite tireless.

I opened up my wireless,
No wonder he was tireless!
I pulled his batteries out, and hey,
No tireless wireless Silas!

You Know!

You know I'm scared
Of creepy things,
And things that cling
And howl and sing
And shout and jump
And bang and bump
And gawp and gape
And scratch and scrape
And sneer and scowl
And grunt and growl
And stop and stare
And fill the air
With ghostly sound
From all around;
You *know* they make me frightened,
So why not leave the light on?

Eerie Feeling

Eerie feeling, scary feeling,
Someone's behind the curtain.
He isn't discreet, as I've spotted his feet,
And he's waiting to get me, I'm certain.

Eerie feeling, scary feeling,
I've entered the Twilight Zone.
It's hard not to scream when you're trapped
   in a dream,
And the feet over there are your *own*!

Hauntingly

Hall

We're all in good spirits at Hauntingly Hall
The home of the rattling chain and the ball.
We're really quite pleased you've decided to call,
So welcome to Hauntingly Hall.

We've opened the shutters at Hauntingly Hall
Where banshees are likely to wail and to bawl
And freak apparitions can walk through a wall,
So welcome to Hauntingly Hall.

We couldn't be prouder at Hauntingly Hall
Our demons and darkness are bound to appal
Our beasts are the finest to slither and crawl,
So welcome to Hauntingly Hall!

Creepy

Beware, beware, of *Creepy*,
Especially when you're sleepy.
You won't be safe in house or hut,
In igloo, tent, or tepee.

When blackest night is falling,
He's at his most appalling.
From Creepy's crypt he's just
   crept out,
To do some Creepy crawling!

Claw

Claw is slithering
Claw is crawling
Gliding
Sliding
To your door.
Claw is moving
Oh, so quietly,
Sifting
Shifting
As before.

Can you hear
His nails outside,
Scratching
Till you
Freeze with fright?
Then suddenly
He's gone, and then
You're safe;
Until
Tomorrow night.

Jekyll and Hyde

When old Master Hyde
Goes out for a meal,
It ends in the usual way;
For sooner or later
He'll growl at the waiter,
And tell him that *Jekyll* will pay!

390,533

I Scream...

Phantoms flit, and fly around,
Witches cackle, Trolls abound.
But do I face them, bold and
mean?
No, I don't; I scream.

Hideous monsters run and crawl,
In my head, I've seen them all.
But do I stop them, as they teem?
No, I don't; I scream.

Once again my nightmare's here,
Every night's a night of fear.
But do I fight it, in my dream?
No, I don't; I *scream*.

Knock Knock!

Knock knock! was the sound that would hold me
  in fear
When the old-fashioned ghost at my door would
  appear.
But all of a sudden
He's getting quite modern,
And now his *Ding-Donging* is all I can hear!

Hiding in my Attic

Hiding in my attic
There's a thing that I deplore,
It seems to lift the furniture,
Then drops it on the floor.
I get the oddest feeling,
Which I've had since it began;
I think it's the ghost of Mister Tripp,
The timid removal man.

I'm much too scared to go upstairs,
He's scared to come back down.
He isn't really helping much
By throwing things around.
I'd like to go and help him
But I don't know if I can.
Who's frightened the most, is it me or the ghost
Of the timid removal man?

No Thank You!

'Pardon?
Would I like a monster
Who's without a place to live?
And could I use a Banshee
Who has lots of love to give?
And do I want a Poltergeist
Who smashes cups and plates?
Or do I want the creature
That you've left outside my gate?
No thank you, I do not,
Most definitely not!
No thank you, I do not,
Because I'll tell you
What I've got:

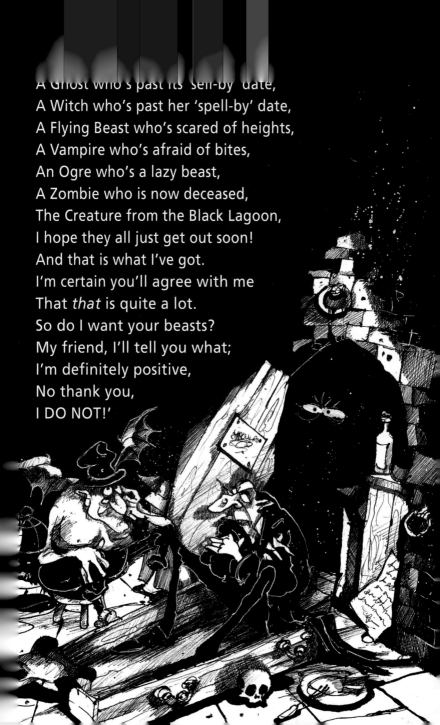

A Ghost who's past its 'sell-by' date,
A Witch who's past her 'spell-by' date,
A Flying Beast who's scared of heights,
A Vampire who's afraid of bites,
An Ogre who's a lazy beast,
A Zombie who is now deceased,
The Creature from the Black Lagoon,
I hope they all just get out soon!
And that is what I've got.
I'm certain you'll agree with me
That *that* is quite a lot.
So do I want your beasts?
My friend, I'll tell you what;
I'm definitely positive,
No thank you,
I DO NOT!'

Bagpipes

Your ghost, dear McTavish
Will drone on the pipes,
As it has for two hundred
And fifty-four years.
I'm always dead wary
Of piping that's scary,
So why not have mercy
And spare my poor ears?

Odd Bod

The facts about Odd Bod
Are crazy but true,
For Odd Bod was fashioned
From parts old and new.
He's got a fish finger
Instead of a nose,
A scientist made him,
But why? Goodness knows!
Instead of real hair
There's electrical wire,
And stuck round his waist
Is a motorbike tyre.
But Odd Bod is punctual
And that's without doubt,
He opens his mouth
And a cuckoo pops out!
In place of a head
A big melon's been put,
Attached to his wrist
Is a size seven foot.
And *that* is the bit
That I don't understand,
I'm sure that poor Odd Bod
Could do with a hand!

Ellen.

At the top of the stair
At the end of the hall,
Is a painted portrait
Which sits on the wall.
The picture of Ellen
Could speak of such doom,
That its eyes even follow you
Into your room.

Her love was a madman
Who wanted her dead,
His greed for her money
Had governed his head.
A flash of insanity
Showed him the way,
And he sealed Lady Ellen
In concrete and clay.

And up to this day
At the top of the stair,
The people that come here
Are still unaware,
That the portrait they stare at
Has grief in its eyes,
For poor Lady Ellen
Behind the wall lies.

29

A Close Shave

A fuzzy-faced Werewolf
Who must have been barmy,
Decided one day
On a life with the army.
He left at the very first
Orders they gave:
'And now, Mister Werewolf,
It's time for your SHAVE!'

Two By Two

Two by two went the ghosts in the church
Who refused to come down from upstairs.
'We'll stay in the steeple,
We're frightened of people,
And that's why we're walking in pairs!'

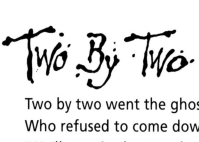

Rest in Pieces

How his family squabbled, when Solomon died!
For where they should bury him, caused a divide.
But then came a brainwave from one of his nieces,
So Solomon Barlow's now resting in pieces.

Weird Sisters Three

Weird sisters three
Are confused, as you see,
When taking a trip
To the market.
There isn't much room
When you're three to a broom,
And you've got no idea
How to park it.

Hobbling Goblin.

A Goblin went out skiing on a night I won't forget,
And speeding down the slopes he travelled,
Frightening all he met.
He fell and broke his leg and lay for hours in the snow,
And now that hobbling Goblin's troubling
No one that I know.

'Auntie, Auntie!'

'Auntie, auntie! We're poltergeists, aren't we?
The kids on the block have been running away
Because of the things that we do every day.
We've got no intention of changing at all,
We thought it was *normal* to walk through a wall!'

'Auntie, auntie! We SHALL be good, shan't we?
We'll try not to frighten the neighbours tonight,
Provided they're careful and leave on a light.
We wouldn't want people to say we were bad,
But moaning and shrieking's the best fun we've had!'

'Auntie, auntie! We CAN behave, can't we?
And just because objects mysteriously fly,
They're calling for vicars and starting to cry.
Though not an exception at all to the rule,
There's surely no harm in us playing the *ghoul*.'

The Dim Reaper

'Your days are now over!' the Grim Reaper said,
And lifting his scythe up, he swung at my head.
But quickly I ducked, and he suffered a shock;
He carried on swinging and chopped his *own* block!

I Love It When I'm Scared

I *love* it when I'm scared.
When ghosts and beasties call around
I'm always quite prepared,
It really makes my night.

I love it when they scream.
When Drac the bat decides to call,
He knows it's been my dream,
To feel a vampire's bite.

I love it when they howl.
For spooks are very grateful things,
And even werewolves growl,
'We didn't know you cared!'

I love it when they grunt.
And even when they say I'm strange
And slightly back to front,
I *love* it when I'm scared!

Hairy Scary

Has nature played a trick on me
To catch me unawares?
For every time the moon is full
I sprout a million hairs!
I've seen a dozen doctors
But it seems that no one cares,
I guess I'm just a hairy scary Werewolf.

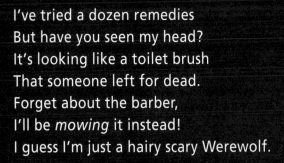

I've tried a dozen remedies
But have you seen my head?
It's looking like a toilet brush
That someone left for dead.
Forget about the barber,
I'll be *mowing* it instead!
I guess I'm just a hairy scary Werewolf.

While standing in a rubbish tip
And howling at the moon,
A group of people captured me,
It could have spelled my doom.
The peasants turned me upside-down
And used me as a broom!
I guess I'm just a hairy scary Werewolf.

Werewolf

I've tried to say I'm sorry
But I'll never make amends,
I'm running out of company
And heartache never ends.
It's getting pretty lonely
As I've eaten half my friends!
I guess I'm just a hairy scary Werewolf.

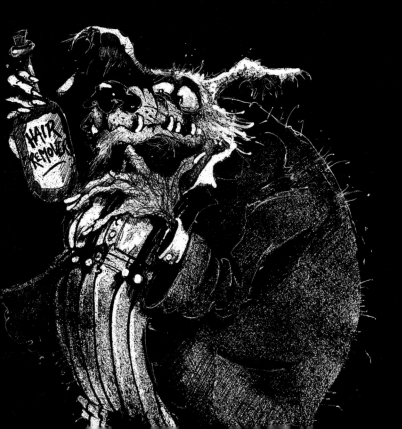

Iceman Cometh

Like a supernatural gladiator,
The *Iceman* cometh!
Shall we stand him near a radiator,
And watch him runneth?

Crazy For You

'I'm crazy for you,'
Said the cat to the raven,
'And though it is cold,
I will give you safe haven.'

'I promise you now,'
Said the cat in the storm,
'That where you'll end up
Will be lovely and warm.'

'My mistress the witch
Is preparing a stew,
And that is why, raven,
I'm crazy for you.'

The Empty House

Don't go into the empty house,
Don't go in at all.
For if you do, and walk within,
You're destined for a fall.
For late one night, when darkness fell,
And stillness was around,
I went inside the empty house,
And *never* was I found.

Beardy Weirdy

Beardy Weirdy's coming to town,
Time to pull the shutters down.
Fifteen feet of straggly beard,
Something about that man is weird.

Creatures live inside that hair.
Beardy Weirdy doesn't care.
Frightens adults, frightens nippers,
Quickly, get the garden clippers!

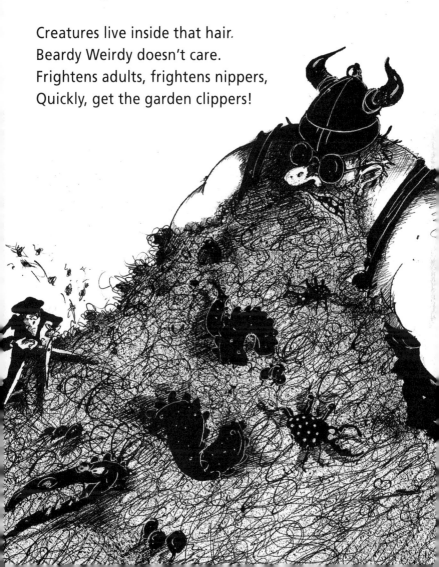

Inviting For Biting

My name is Mister Dracula
But you can call me Drac.
I'd love to be more popular
And gain the friends I lack.
While looking in my mirror
On a cold and frosty morn,
I noticed there was *no one*
And it then began to dawn.
I'm searching for companions
Who aren't too quick to vex,
And do not mind protruding fangs
Or bite marks on their necks.
I'm glad you're so agreeable,
I'll make it worth your while,
You're more relaxed than certain folk
Who tend to run a mile.

I hope that I can count on you
Of course, I'll see you're paid,
It's just that I get thirsty,
And it's not for lemonade!
But please don't bring a garlic snack,
It's sure to make me cross;
The only thing I'll need is *you*,
And lots of dental floss.
And please don't let my castle doors
Alarm you when they THUD!
I only crave your company,
Well *that*, and pints of blood!

The Hobbledinob

The Hobbledinob stayed home last night,
He decided he just couldn't risk it.
For how can a beast
Make you scared in the least
When his name sounds a bit like a biscuit?

You're Probably Mad

Is Frankenstein getting too big for his boots?
Has the Yeti been leaving you cold?
Is the man in the tomb with the bandages on,
In need of his Mummy to hold?

Is Dracula lacking his usual bite?
Is the Zombie less scary than Dad?
For if none of these creatures can spook you at all,
Then I reckon you're probably mad.

Loch Less

I spoke to the beast from Loch Ness,
Who told me, 'Och aye, I confess!
I've swallowed a whaler,
Two ships, and a sailor,
And frankly, I couldn't care less!'

It

It keeps me awake at night.
It troubles my mind.
It frightens me.
It plays on my fears.
It laughs a fiendish laugh.
It knows me, and
It waits for me.
It taps on my window.
It knocks on my door.
It shakes at my ceiling.
It scrapes on my floor.
It seems to call my name, and
It never leaves me alone.

It…is my imagination.

Bad Hairwolf

While recently out for a jog,
A Werewolf approached in the fog,
I took him back home
And lent him a comb,
But still he looks worse than my dog!

Dead Right

In summer, to keep himself cool
A ghost took a swim in my pool.
I shouted, 'You'll drown,
By splashing around!'
He said, 'It's too late, you old fool!'

I Chews You

I've recently married a beast
Who hardly offends in the least.
Our wedding was nice,
She spat out the rice
And chewed the left ear off the priest!

Prince Vlad

My cousin, Prince Vlad the Impaler,
Has lately been looking much frailer.
Since wheezing and coughing
Reduced him to nothing,
They're calling him Vlad the *Inhaler*.

Sweeney

Todd Horner

Sweeney Todd Horner
Sat in a corner,
Eating a Christmas pie;
Instead of a plum
He pulled out a *thumb*,
And said, 'What a demon am I!'

Drac and Jill

Drac and Jill went up the hill
To fetch a pail of water,
Drac felt pangs
And showed his fangs;
Jill ran, but Drac still caught her!

Scary Mary

'Scary Mary, quite contrary,
How does your graveyard grow?'

'With Monsters, Kooks, assorted Spooks,
And headstones all in a row row row,
And headstones all in a row.'

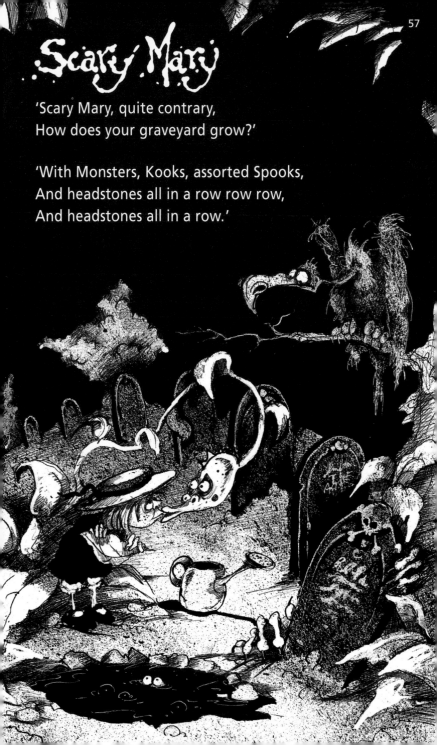

Diablo D. Wright

His name is Diablo, Diablo D. Wright,
A teacher by day, but a devil by night.

They put him in charge of unruly Year Six,
Who from the beginning got up to their tricks.
They promised that soon he'd be running a mile,
But no one had noticed his sinister smile.
They taunted and teased him, and said he was weird,
Then started to laugh at his small pointed beard.
They threw paper planes, which were aimed at his
    head,
Then suddenly realized his eyes had turned *red*.
The classroom grew hot, and they started to wail,
Imagine the shock when he next grew a *tail*!
And then with a sweep of his crimson-red cloak,
Year Six disappeared in a big puff of smoke!
(But don't be afraid, they were back the next day,
Behaving like *angels* indeed, some would say.)

His name is Diablo, Diablo D. Wright,
A teacher by day, but a *devil* by night.

Tap on Your Shoulder

What could be worse
Than a tap on your shoulder
At Witching Hour,
When the air has grown colder
Than icicles hanging
From a goblin's nose,
And you are alone,
But nobody knows?

What could be worse
Than a tap on your shoulder
At Haunting Hour?
Has nobody told you
That gremlins and gargoyles
Go mad in the night,
And reach out and grab
If you come within sight?

What could be worse
Than a tap on your shoulder?

A sink on your head.

Baskerville Hound.

The Baskerville Hound is at home;
It's better to leave him alone.
He lives in a cupboard
And even Ma Hubbard
Is frightened to give him a bone!

The End

They tell me the ending is nigh,
For even ghost poems can die.
The trapdoor is open
And though I was hoping
To stay a bit longer, 'Goodb...'